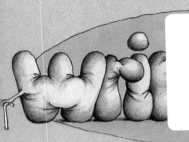

Rule Ok!

LOOK... IF I WAKE THE CAT—I WAKE THE CAT

SILVEY-JEX

Books by Boxer:
Swinnow Lane, Bramley,
Leeds, UK LS13 4BS

Tel: 01133 955 593
Fax: 01133 955 594
email: sales@booksbyboxer.com
Web: www.booksbyboxer.com

ISBN 9781909732070
Item Code: YOA0006

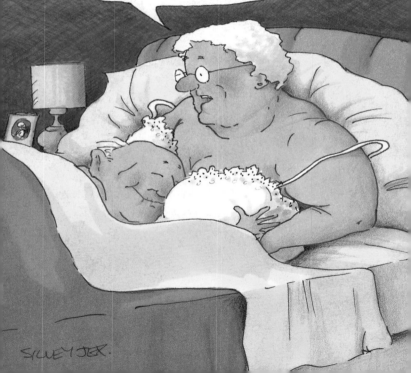

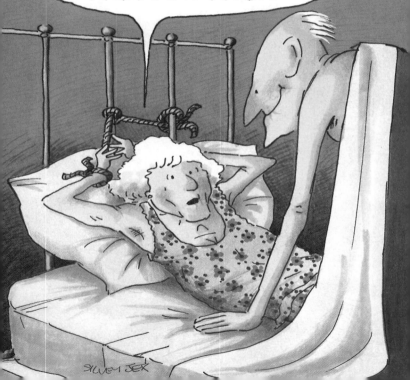

HELLO...I'M YOUR BLIND DATE
ARE YOU? THEN HOWEVER DID YOU FIND ME?
URANT

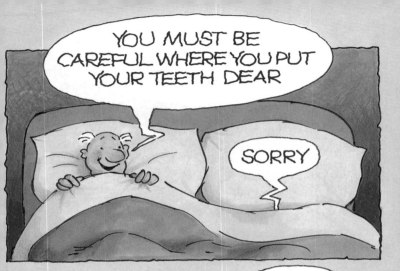

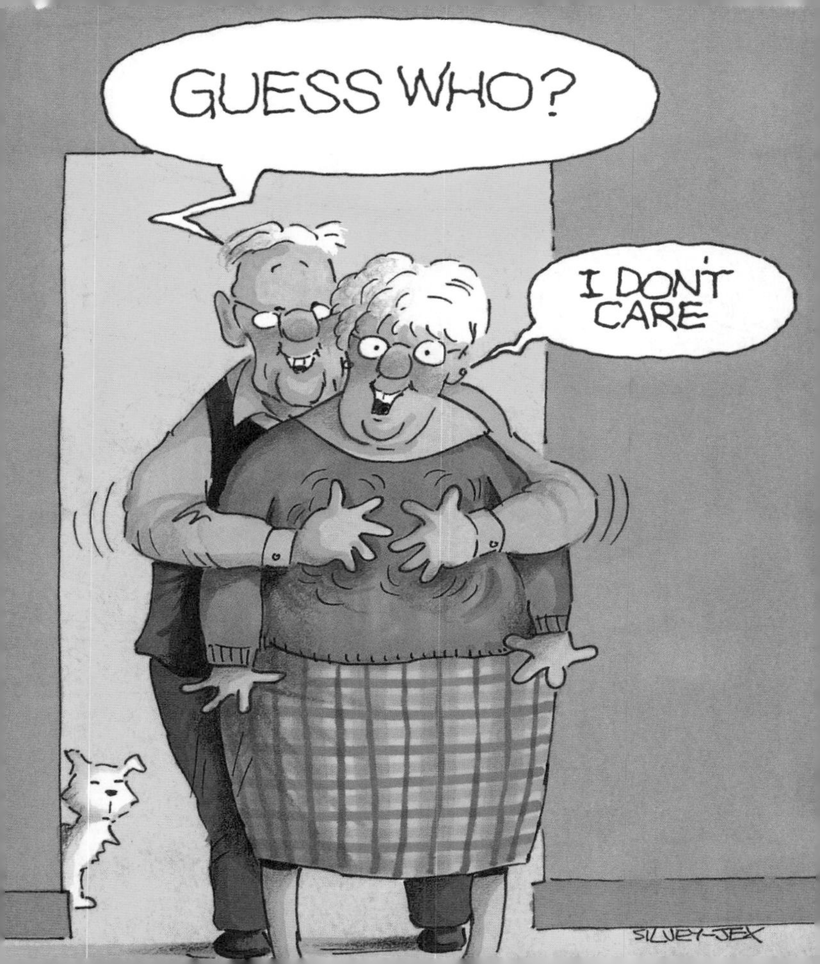
GUESS WHO?
I DON'T CARE
SILVEY-JEX

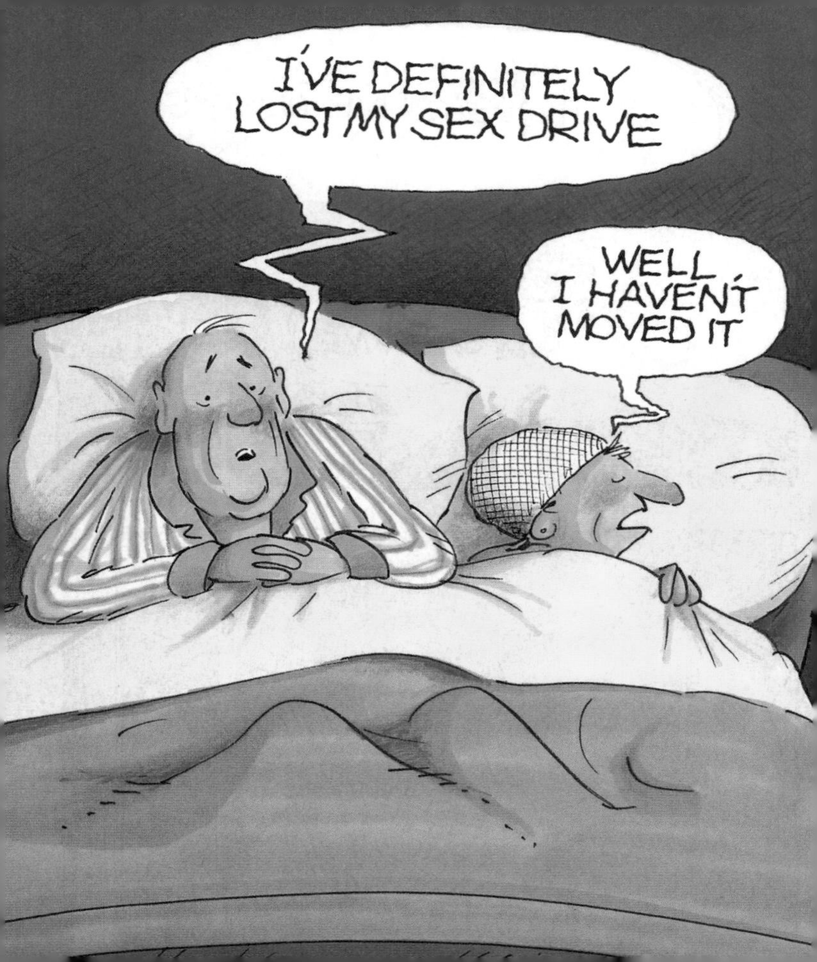
I'VE DEFINITELY LOST MY SEX DRIVE
WELL I HAVEN'T MOVED IT